"THE CRACKED EGG SERIES"

TEN FUN WAYS TO CREATE THE MAGIC IN YOU

"Believe in yourself & make your dreams come true."

BOOK FOUR

written and illustrated by
LINDA C. BRYANT

 LC Productions

Ten Fun Ways to Create the Magic in You
Copyright © 1992 by Linda C. Bryant

LC Productions
119-5th Street, Suite B-101
Wenatchee, WA 98801
800-274-2130

Printed and bound in the United States of America.
Also available in French, German, Japanese, Russian and Spanish.

Library of Congress No. 92-85115

ISBN #1-881232-04-2

Books by Linda C. Bryant

"The Cracked Egg Series"
Ten Fun Ways to Come Out of Your Shell
Ten Fun Ways to Feel Better About Yourself
Ten Fun Ways to View the Real You
Ten Fun Ways to Create the Magic in You

Upcoming Series by Linda C. Bryant

"Talents Unlimited for Kids"
"Out of Your Shell and Shining Bright"

This series is dedicated to ...

Christopher Michael (Chris) and
Jonathan Paul (Jon) —
my sons, and two of my best friends.

Table of Contents

Note to the 'Adult Kid' or Parent . . .

Magic! For a lot of **older kids** it may be thought of being only in fairy tales. However, magic is all around you everyday in many forms.

Magic is the physical result grown or produced from the birth of a desired idea and believing in its being and having it finally come true.

Remember this as you begin: Magic results from what is done. (Like many say: **Just Do It!**)

Linda

Just For Kids...

Magic happening in your life takes more than just the snap of your fingers — but it can **happen**!

Simple ways in this book lead you to learn how. What happens depends only on YOU by <u>what</u> you "DO."

Have fun making your dreams come true!

Linda

HOW TO USE THIS BOOK !

1. ATTITUDE CHECK-IN
2. RULES OF THE ROAD
3. THE 'NO NEED TO BUY' SUPPLY LIST
4. BUDDY-UP !

   GO

~ 1 ~

ATTITUDE

LOVE LIFE & HAVE FUN !

(This is not a chore.)

BE UPBEAT and HAPPY !

(Even if you have to practice this at first,
the more you do it, the easier it gets.)

CHALLENGE YOURSELF !

(Go through the entire day
using this new attitude.)

RULES OF THE ROAD:

FUN

FUN

FUN

DO ALL THE STEPS EVERYDAY !

(Remember — WHO WANTS A DAY OFF FROM FUN ?)

Fill in one line per day.

~ 3 ~

THE 'NO NEED TO BUY' SUPPLY LIST

IF YOU DO NOT HAVE ANY OF THE FOLLOWING, BORROW FROM SOMEONE THAT DOES:

1. A big mirror you can use by yourself at least two (2) times a day.

2. Pen or pencil to write daily in your book. (The more you write in it, the more good comes from it !)

~ 4 ~

BUDDY-UP !

1. Get a good 'friend' and do some of the 'ways' together. Sharing these things about you helps them to know you better and you them.

2. Get an 'adult' you care about to do this with you ! ! !

GO FOR IT

and

LET THE FUN BEGIN !

LIST THINGS YOU WOULD LIKE BETTER OR CHANGED IN YOUR LIFE.

(This is for future reference.)

★ <u>better at soccer</u>   ★ _____

≫→ _____   ≫→ _____

! _____   ! _____

❤ _____   ❤ _____

★ _____   ★ _____

≫→ _____   ≫→ _____

! _____   ! _____

❤ _____   ❤ _____

★ _____   ★ _____

≫→ _____   ≫→ _____

! _____   ! _____

❤ _____   ❤ _____

~ 1 ~

NO BATTERIES NEEDED

~ 1 ~

I AM SELF-POWERED !

I OPERATE WITHOUT BATTERIES !

IDENTIFY A PHYSICAL THING
you did today that does not take thinking or planning to do it.

(e.g., Turning to look at something.)

1. _____
2. _____
3. _____
4. _____
5. _____
6. _____
7. _____
8. _____
9. _____
10. _____
11. _____
12. _____
13. _____
14. _____
15. _____

~ 1 ~

MORE OF WHAT YOU DO
physically without thinking or
planning — it just happens !

16. _____

17. _____

18. _____

19. _____

20. _____

21. _____

22. _____

23. _____

24. _____

25. _____

26. _____

27. _____

28. _____

29. _____

30. _____

This way to #2

~ 2 ~

WISH OUT LOUD

～ 2 ～

MAKE A WISH and say it OUT LOUD!

JUST REMEMBER:
Have it be good for you —
life moves in the direction
of your ordered wish.

～ 2 ～

WISH ORDER FORM
(Part 1)
Fill out in detail below.

Day	Your Wish	Itemized Description	What can it do for you that's good?
1			
2			
3			
4			
5			
6			
7			
8			
9			
10			

~ 2 ~

WISH ORDER FORM

(Part 2)

Fill out in detail below.

What do you expect by having it?	Will you settle for anything less as 2nd choice?		What, then, is 2nd choice?	Can you live with 2nd choice forever?		If you checked 'yes'	If you checked 'no'
	Yes	No		Yes	No		
						EXPECT IT !	WISH AGAIN !

~ 2 ~

WISH ORDER FORM
(Part 1)
Fill out in detail below.

Day	Your Wish	Itemized Description	What can it do for you that's good
11			
12			
13			
14			
15			
16			
17			
18			
19			
20			

~ 2 ~

WISH ORDER FORM
(Part 2)
Fill out in detail below.

What do you expect by having it?	Will you settle for anything less as 2nd choice?		What, then, is 2nd choice?	Can you live with 2nd choice forever?		If you checked 'yes'	If you checked 'no'
	Yes	No		Yes	No	EXPECT IT !	WISH AGAIN !

~ 2 ~

WISH ORDER FORM
(Part 1)
Fill out in detail below.

Day	Your Wish	Itemized Description	What can it do for you that's good?
21			
22			
23			
24			
25			
26			
27			
28			
29			
30			

~ 2 ~

WISH ORDER FORM
(Part 2)

hat do you expect by having it?	Will you settle for anything less as 2nd choice?		What, then, is 2nd choice?	Can you live with 2nd choice forever?		If you checked 'yes'	If you checked 'no'
	Yes	No		Yes	No	EXPECT IT !	WISH AGAIN !

This way to #3

~ 3 ~

SECRET PAL

~ 3 ~

YOUR SECRET PAL IS THERE ALL THE TIME
in your heart and
in your mind !

Ask your secret pal
what you can do physically
so that you move towards
your wish coming true.

~ 3 ~

ASK & LISTEN.
Write it down daily.

1. _____
2. _____
3. _____
4. _____
5. _____
6. _____
7. _____
8. _____
9. _____
10. _____
11. _____
12. _____
13. _____
14. _____
15. _____

~ 3 ~

REMEMBER YOUR SECRET PAL INSIDE — ASK & LISTEN.
Write it down.

16. _____

17. _____

18. _____

19. _____

20. _____

21. _____

22. _____

23. _____

24. _____

25. _____

26. _____

27. _____

28. _____

29. _____

30. _____

This way to #4

~ 4 ~

TEAM UP — PLAY BALL

~ 4 ~

PICK YOUR OWN TEAM TO PLAY 'THE GAME OF YOUR LIFE' !

<u>WHO</u> do you want?

<u>WHAT</u> do you need?

<u>WHEN</u> it's forever !

<u>WHERE</u> will you go?

<u>HOW</u> can you do it in the best way you know, now?

It's your own MAGIC team — BE PICKY !

～ 4 ～

DAILY GAME PLAN
(Part 1)

Day	Who	What	When
1			
2			
3			
4			
5			
6			
7			
8			
9			
10			
11			
12			
13			
14			
15			

~ 4 ~

DAILY GAME PLAN
(Part 2)

Where	How

DAILY GAME PLAN
(Part 1)

Day	Who	What	When
16			
17			
18			
19			
20			
21			
22			
23			
24			
25			
26			
27			
28			
29			
30			

~ 4 ~

DAILY GAME PLAN
(Part 2)

Where	How

This way to #5

~ 5 ~

A 'KID' AT HEART

~ 5 ~

<u>BE</u> A 'KID' AT HEART.

TAKE TIME OUT TODAY — JUST TO PLAY.

Do something fun !

~ 5 ~

Think on ways to add more ENTHUSIASM & FUN to your day.

List some ideas that you like.

1. _____   _____
2. _____   _____
3. _____   _____
4. _____   _____
5. _____   _____
6. _____   _____
7. _____   _____
8. _____   _____
9. _____   _____
10. _____   _____
11. _____   _____
12. _____   _____
13. _____   _____
14. _____   _____
15. _____   _____

~ 5 ~

Keep listing the
ENTHUSIASTIC & FUN ways.

(Your 'secret pal' can help you.)

16. _____   _____
17. _____   _____
18. _____   _____
19. _____   _____
20. _____   _____
21. _____   _____
22. _____   _____
23. _____   _____
24. _____   _____
25. _____   _____
26. _____   _____
27. _____   _____
28. _____   _____
29. _____   _____
30. _____   _____

This way to #6

~ 6 ~

MAGNETIC ATTRACTION

~ 6 ~

(say out loud)

"TODAY — I ATTRACT MORE OF MY WISH TO ME, BY ACTING AS IF IT IS ALREADY A PART OF ME!"

You will then be moving towards and attracting your wish closer to you.

~ 6 ~

<u>WHAT</u> YOU PHYSICALLY DID
today that related directly
to accomplishing your wish.

1. _____
2. _____
3. _____
4. _____
5. _____
6. _____
7. _____
8. _____
9. _____
10. _____
11. _____
12. _____
13. _____
14. _____
15. _____

~ 6 ~

MORE OF — <u>WHAT</u> YOU DID
that related directly to the wish you focused on.

16. _____
17. _____
18. _____
19. _____
20. _____
21. _____
22. _____
23. _____
24. _____
25. _____
26. _____
27. _____
28. _____
29. _____
30. _____

Look what else you attracted related to your wish for having done this physical move.

(This happens after you actually DO something towards it yourself.)

1. _____
2. _____
3. _____
4. _____
5. _____
6. _____
7. _____
8. _____
9. _____
10. _____
11. _____
12. _____
13. _____
14. _____
15. _____

~ 6 ~

Actions by you towards your wish gathers
more related stages to it being real.

(List below.)

16. _____
17. _____
18. _____
19. _____
20. _____
21. _____
22. _____
23. _____
24. _____
25. _____
26. _____
27. _____
28. _____
29. _____
30. _____

This way to #7

~7~

OPEN THE DOOR

~ 7 ~

INSIDE YOUR HEART IS A SPECIAL DOOR

TO A ROOM WHERE YOUR WISHES COME TRUE.

OPEN IT . . .
see yourself there !

~ 7 ~

WRITE A POSITIVE REMINDER
of your wish each day —
after seeing it in your mind.

1. _____
2. _____
3. _____
4. _____
5. _____
6. _____
7. _____
8. _____
9. _____
10. _____
11. _____
12. _____
13. _____
14. _____
15. _____

~ 7 ~

MORE POSITIVE REMINDERS
of your wish each day —
after seeing it in your mind.

16. _____

17. _____

18. _____

19. _____

20. _____

21. _____

22. _____

23. _____

24. _____

25. _____

26. _____

27. _____

28. _____

29. _____

30. _____

This way to #8

~ 8 ~

WISHING IS LIKE
FISHING

~ 8 ~

BE STILL, BE PATIENT, BE FOCUSED, BE THANKFUL !

YOU MAY NOT HAVE IT NOW,
BUT JUST WAIT . . .
EVENTUALLY IT WILL COME !

~ 8 ~

BE STILL — FOCUS CLEARLY ON THE WISH YOU ORDERED

List any or all parts you thankfully physically caught today.

1. _____
2. _____
3. _____
4. _____
5. _____
6. _____
7. _____
8. _____
9. _____
10. _____
11. _____
12. _____
13. _____
14. _____
15. _____

~ 8 ~

CONTINUE TO KEEP FISHING !

(And list below — daily.)

16. _____

17. _____

18. _____

19. _____

20. _____

21. _____

22. _____

23. _____

24. _____

25. _____

26. _____

27. _____

28. _____

29. _____

30. _____

This way to #9

~ 9 ~

USE THE MAGIC WAND

~ 9 ~

IN YOUR MIND THINK OF SOMETHING 'GOOD'

for someone close to you that they want to do or have.

See them as already having it !

Be excited & happy for them receiving their wish, too !

~ 9 ~

<u>WHO</u> IS IT YOU USED YOUR MAGIC WAND ON?

Think of someone each day.
Write their name below.

1. _____
2. _____
3. _____
4. _____
5. _____
6. _____
7. _____
8. _____
9. _____
10. _____
11. _____
12. _____
13. _____
14. _____
15. _____

16. _____
17. _____
18. _____
19. _____
20. _____
21. _____
22. _____
23. _____
24. _____
25. _____
26. _____
27. _____
28. _____
29. _____
30. _____

~ 9 ~

<u>WHAT</u> IS IT THEY WISHED FOR THAT YOU SEE THEM HAVING?

List it below.
(Remember — What you wish good for others comes back in other ways just for you !)

1. _____
2. _____
3. _____
4. _____
5. _____
6. _____
7. _____
8. _____
9. _____
10. _____
11. _____
12. _____
13. _____
14. _____
15. _____

16. _____
17. _____
18. _____
19. _____
20. _____
21. _____
22. _____
23. _____
24. _____
25. _____
26. _____
27. _____
28. _____
29. _____
30. _____

This way to #10

～ 10 ～

WISHES COME TRUE

∼ 10 ∼

EVERY DAY, EVERY WAY
YOUR WISHES COME TRUE.

But you must let go of them
in order to bring them
back to you !

～ 10 ～

USE YOUR WISHING WELL.

Lower the bucket (letting go) and pull it back
up — gathering more of your wish to you.

1. _____

2. _____

3. _____

4. _____

5. _____

6. _____

7. _____

8. _____

9. _____

10. _____

~ 10 ~

WHAT PARTS OF YOUR WISH CAME TO YOU TODAY ?

Every day look for the magic
of them appearing.

11. _____
_____

12. _____
_____

13. _____
_____

14. _____
_____

15. _____
_____

16. _____
_____

17. _____
_____

18. _____
_____

19. _____
_____

20. _____
_____

Keep going ! ⋙→

~ 10 ~

STILL WATCH AND
KEEP TRACK EACH DAY.

21. _____
_____
22. _____
_____
23. _____
_____
24. _____
_____
25. _____
_____
26. _____
_____
27. _____
_____
28. _____
_____
29. _____
_____
30. _____
_____

Remember: WISHES DO COME TRUE !

From the Author . . .

That's me, Linda. I follow these techniques to make my life accomplishments fun and allow myself to perform a multitude of talented abilities developed over the years. The results I experienced (along with a lot of phone calls from people asking, "How do you do it?"), prompted me to write these books.

One important fact about me is that I encourage you to know about yourself. Those techniques are what I share in this series of books.

My life so far contains a lot of basics: Birth certificate from the state of Washington, report cards, driver's license, graduation diplomas, an official "press pass," and a first aid instructor's card — just to name a few. All these rites of passage have been great, including the one I gave myself, forming my own company — LC PRODUCTIONS.

Living and teaching what I take as a stand in life, that of wise self-reliance. I look forward to finding the cosmic chuckle in each new day. It's great!

May each of you look forward to finding the fun in life daily.

Linda C. Bryant

"THE CRACKED EGG SERIES"

Written and illustrated by Linda C. Bryant

UNIQUE NEW BOOKS — Individually focused —
Encourage breaking out of your shell
and promote progressive growth from wherever you are in life.

❑ Book 1 – TEN FUN WAYS TO COME OUT OF YOUR SHELL
"Unique activities to help promote positive thinking." *$11.95*

❑ Book 2 – TEN FUN WAYS TO FEEL BETTER ABOUT YOURSELF
"Encourages balanced well-being." *$11.95*

❑ Book 3 – TEN FUN WAYS TO VIEW THE REAL YOU
"Clarify and enjoy self-worth using your special talents." *$11.95*

❑ Book 4 – TEN FUN WAYS TO CREATE THE MAGIC IN YOU
"Believe in yourself & make your dreams come true." *$11.95*

LC Productions, 119-5th Street, Suite B-101, Wenatchee, WA 98801

Please send the items I have checked above. I am enclosing $____________.
(Add $1.00 plus $.50 each additional title for postage and handling. WA residents add 7.9% sales tax.) Send check or money order, no cash or C.O.D.s please.

Name ______________________________________

Address ______________________________________

City/State ____________________ Zip ____________

Daytime Phone (   ) ______________

❑ Visa ❑ MasterCard

Exp. Date ____________ Signature __________________

Please allow 4-6 weeks for delivery.

All titles also available in French, German, Japanese, Russian and Spanish.
For pricing and ordering information, call 1-800-274-2130.

Prices and availability subject to change without notice.

✂ Please cut or tear along line.

NOTES

NOTES

NOTES

NOTES

NOTES

NOTES

NOTES

NOTES

NOTES

NOTES

NOTES